## D Look at the graph. Answer the questions.

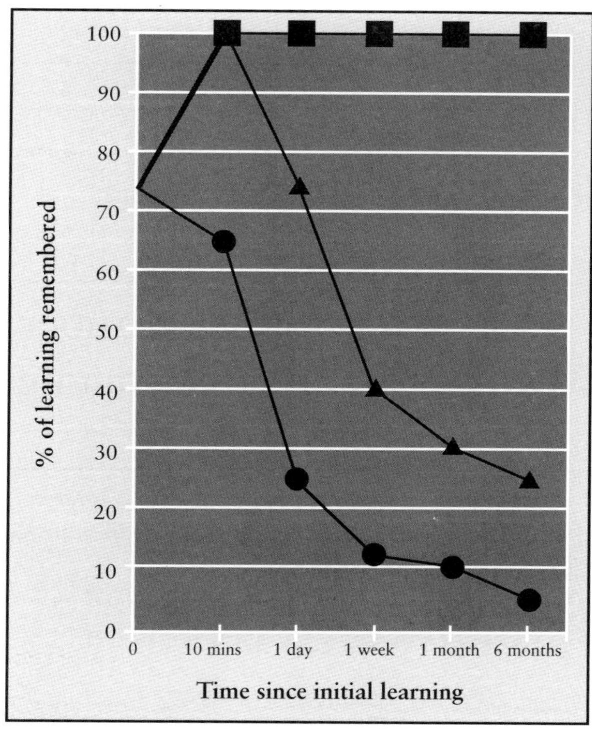


green = % with regular revision

blue = % with one revision

red = % with no revision

Source: Education Research Council

**Example:**

1 What does the graph show?

*The percentage of learning remembered.*

2 What does the red line show?

______________________________

3 What about the green line?

______________________________

4 How much do you remember after one week with no revision?

______________________________

5 According to the graph, how can you remember information for ever?

______________________________

6 Where is this information from?

______________________________

**(10 marks)**

**E You are going to read a text about learning a foreign language.**

1 Read the heading. Think of two answers.

______________________________

______________________________

**(4 marks)**

2 Read the introduction and topic sentences 1–4. Where will you find the following information?

**Example:**

| The topic of the text | *Intro* |
|---|---|
| An explanation of the 'Language Town' idea | |
| A definition of mnemonics | |
| Some useful words to learn | |
| Some ways to connect words in different languages | |

**(8 marks)**

# How Can You Remember Words in a Foreign Language?

*Imagine you want to start learning a foreign language. Are there any ways to help your brain keep new words in memory?*

1 The first point, of course, is to learn useful words.

2 The second way to help your brain is to connect words in a foreign language to words in your own language.

3 Thirdly, you can use mnemonics to help your brain remember.

4 One mnemonic idea for language learning is to think of 'Language Town'.

**F Read paragraph 1 of the text.**

1 Write five words from Buzan's list.

______________________________

______________________________

______________________________

______________________________

______________________________

2 Think of five more words that might be in the list.

______________________________

______________________________

______________________________

______________________________

______________________________

**(12 marks)**

**G Read paragraph 2 of the text.**

1 What is 1, 2, 3 in Italian? ______________________________

2 Four in Italian is *quattro*. How could an English speaker remember this word?

______________________________

**(10 marks)**

**H** **Read paragraph 3 of the text.**

The colours of the rainbow in order are *red, orange, yellow, green, blue, violet, indigo*.
Think of a mnemonic for this.

______________________________________________________________

**(6 marks)**

**I** **Read paragraph 4 of the text. What else could you have in each of these places? Think of two words in each case.**

| | |
|---|---|
| 1 the park | |
| 2 the sports centre | |
| 3 the street | |

**(12 marks)**

**J** **What is the main idea of the text? Tick (✓) the best answer.**

1 Learn the first 100 words and practise them in town. ____

2 Learn useful words, link them to words in your own language or think of a way to remember them. ____

3 Learn the first 100 words, then the numbers, then the colours, then the action verbs, and finally food words. ____

**(8 marks)**

| **Marks out of 100.** | % |
|---|---|

**A Match the words and meanings. Be careful! There is one extra meaning that you don't need.**

**Example:**

| |  | |  |
|---|---|---|---|
| 1 | club | ______ | all the buildings and land of a university |
| 2 | campus | ______ | an idea of how something works in real life |
| 3 | board game | ______ | how much one person does, or gives, in a particular case |
| 4 | parent | ______ | a particular approach to a field of study |
| 5 | model | *1* | a place where people meet socially, often to play games |
| 6 | school | ______ | not children |
| 7 | arise | ______ | believe that something is true |
| 8 | accept | ______ | like snakes and ladders, chess, draughts |
| 9 | contribution | ______ | a mother or father |
| | | ______ | happen, occur |

**(8 marks)**

**B Find and copy nine words in the wordsearch. You can read → ↘ ↗.**

**Example:**

| L | N | V | S | W | H | U | S | B | A | N | D | N |
|---|---|---|---|---|---|---|---|---|---|---|---|---|
| R | T | G | Y | T | M | K | B | N | L | J | O | P |
| R | E | L | A | T | I | O | N | S | H | I | P | T |
| J | W | N | Z | E | N | M | E | Q | T | C | T | W |
| F | Q | P | F | R | I | S | U | C | D | S | X | T |
| B | Z | I | K | L | N | N | A | L | I | W | Y | T |
| L | W | J | B | O | H | S | F | S | U | J | G | K |
| Q | B | V | P | K | N | W | Y | E | P | S | Z | K |
| K | F | S | F | A | T | L | Q | V | R | B | N | P |
| F | E | K | R | H | A | N | R | H | K | I | T | R |
| R | K | T | L | N | X | K | X | B | N | L | O | H |
| W | R | Z | A | M | C | M | N | K | X | R | Q | R |
| P | S | Y | C | H | I | A | T | R | Y | D | Z | M |

*wife* ______ *1*

______ __

______ __

______ __

______ __

______ __

______ __

______ __

______ __

**(8 marks)**

**C The teacher is going to show you the words from Question B. Write the number of each word in the space above.**

**Example:**

You see: *wife*

You write: *1* beside *wife*

**(8 marks)**

**D Copy a word from Question B into each space.**

**Example:**

1 What's the name of his *wife*? I've forgotten.

2 He's her second ____________________. She divorced her first one last year.

3 They have a very interesting ____________________.

4 She says something quite normal, like 'Where's my bag?', but it is often the ____________________ for very strange behaviour from him.

5 His ____________________ will be something like 'I haven't touched it!'

6 She's quite rich and I think he feels ____________________ to her.

7 It's quite bad. He should probably go for ____________________.

8 But I don't think he believes in ____________________.

**(7 marks)**

**E You are going to read a text about marriage.**

Read the introduction and topic sentences 1–6.
What do you expect to find in each paragraph?

**Example:**

| Para | Contents |
|---|---|
| 1 | *the different types of marriage* |
| 2 | |
| 3 | |
| 4 | |
| 5 | |
| 6 | |

**(10 marks)**

***Psychiatrists recognize that there are very few perfect relationships. People get married for all sorts of reasons, and it is often many months or years after the wedding before the true nature of the relationship emerges.***

1 According to psychiatrists, marriages can be divided into three types.

2 Apparently, all three kinds of marriage can be successful.

3 There can be many examples from public life of child–child and parent–child marriages.

4 McCartney married for the first time in 1969.

5 McCartney remarried in 2002.

6 Psychiatry can sometimes give us an insight into the behaviour of people around us.

**F Read paragraph 1 and paragraph 2 of the text. Complete Table 1.**

1 List the types of marriage, according to psychiatrists.
2 Give the main characteristic of each type.
3 Give the main reason or reasons for failure of each type.

Table 1: *Types of marriage*

| Type | Main characteristic | Main reason(s) for failure |
|---|---|---|
| | | |
| | | |
| | | |

**(18 marks)**

**G Read the rest of the text. Explain, in one paragraph in your own words, why Paul McCartney is a good example for the writer of this article.**

______________________________

______________________________

______________________________

______________________________

______________________________

**(10 marks)**

**H Decide if each of these points from the text is a fact (*F*) or an opinion (*O*). Mark each sentence *F* or *O*. If it is not clear, put *?* and explain. For opinions, show (in the final column) which word or phrase helped you decide.**

**Example:**

| | | |
|---|---|---|
| 1 This is an article about marriage and relationships. | *F* | |
| 2 There are very few perfect relationships. | *O* | *recognize* |
| 3 Marriage can be divided into three types. | | |
| 4 All three kinds of marriage can be successful. | | |
| 5 The parent–child relationship works if one partner is prepared to play the child, for ever. | | |
| 6 Pop singers often end up in child–child marriages. | | |
| 7 McCartney has been married twice. | | |
| 8 The marital relationships of McCartney are good examples of two types of marriage. | | |
| 9 McCartney married for the first time in 1969. | | |
| 10 The marriage to Linda Eastman was very happy. | | |
| 11 He was even richer and more famous when he married for the second time. | | |
| 12 Psychiatry can help us understand relationships in the real world. | | |

**(20 marks)**

**I Can you apply any information from this text to the real world?**

______________________________

______________________________

______________________________

______________________________

______________________________

**(11 marks)**

| **Marks out of 100.** | **%** |
|---|---|

**A Find and copy ten words in the word snake connected with work and business.**

decidebenefitcareeremployableexperiencequalificationsolutionrequirementdemocraticlogical

**Example:**

*decide* ___ *1* ___ ______________ ___

______________ ___ ______________ ___

______________ ___ ______________ ___

______________ ___ ______________ ___

______________ ___ ______________ ___

**(9 marks)**

**B The teacher is going to show you the words from Question A. Write the number of each word in the space above.**

**Example:**

You see: *decide*

You write: *1* beside *decide*

**(9 marks)**

**C Match the words and meanings.**

**Example:**

| | | | |
|---|---|---|---|
| 1 | evaluate | ______ | a way of doing something with a number of stages |
| 2 | process | ______ | produce something real, or an idea |
| 3 | select | ______ | a person who controls an organization without taking advice from anybody; a dictator |
| 4 | acronym | ______ | another possibility |
| 5 | generate | *1* | decide the value of something |
| 6 | alternative | ______ | choose |
| 7 | autocrat | ______ | the first letters of a number of words put together to make a word, e.g., W.H.O. |

**(12 marks)**

**D You are going to read a text about management.**

1 Read the heading and the subheading. Can you work out the topic of the article?

__________________________________________

__________________________________________

__________________________________________

__________________________________________

__________________________________________

__________________________________________

__________________________________________

__________________________________________

__________________________________________

__________________________________________

2 Study the table that accompanies the article. Check/correct your ideas from question 1 above.

**(6 marks)**

# MBAs need MBO

## The SMAARRT way to get things done

**Table 1: *SMAARRT – The questions***

| | |
|---|---|
| What exactly do we want to do? | Specific |
| How can we find out if we have done it? | Measurable |
| Is it possible to do it? | Achievable |
| Do people accept the objective? | Agreed |
| Does it help us reach our main objective? | Relevant |
| Does it fit in with other objectives? | Related |
| When should we achieve it by? | Time limited |

***There is an old saying: 'If you want something doing, do it yourself'. But even if you have an MBA (Masters in Business Administration), that is not an option when you get into management. Indeed, one definition of management is 'getting things done by other people'. Managers must delegate, or they will never achieve all the objectives of their company or their department. But how can you make sure that other people do things correctly? One answer is MBO, or Management by Objectives.***

1 The term 'Management by Objectives' was coined by the great management theorist Peter Drucker in the 1950s.

2 The basic idea is very simple.

3 Management by objectives is very different from simply assigning tasks.

4 MBO only works if the objective is SMAARRT.

**E Read the introduction and topic sentences 1–4. Where will you find the following information?**

**Example:**

| | |
|---|---|
| The topic of the text | *Intro* |
| A comparison between MBO and other management styles | |
| The origins of MBO | |
| An explanation of the acronym SMAARRT | |
| An explanation of the acronym MBO | |

**(8 marks)**

**F** Read paragraph 1 of the text.

1 MBO is well-known in Britain and the United States. What evidence can you find for this in the text?

___

2 Is MBO practised in other countries? Explain your answer.

___

**(6 marks)**

**G** Read paragraph 2 of the text. Complete Table 2 with ✓ or ?.

**Example:**

Table 2: *MBO in practice*

| Stage | Manager | Employee |
|---|---|---|
| D | ✓ | |
| I | | |
| G | | |
| E | | |
| S | | |
| T | | |

**(10 marks)**

**H** Read paragraph 3 of the text. Explain the saying in this paragraph in your own words, as it relates to MBO.

___

___

___

___

**(8 marks)**

**I** Read paragraph 4 of the text. Write the correct word from SMAARRT in each space.

**Example:**

| | |
|---|---|
| The sales employees have voted to accept the new sales targets. | |
| This will enable us to increase overall profit. | |
| We want to increase our number of sales people. | |
| We increased sales by 15% last year. | |
| We want to achieve the increase in sales by the end of next year. | |
| We want to increase sales by 10%. | *Specific* |
| We will compare monthly sales next year with monthly sales in this year. | |

**(12 marks)**

**J** **Find these sections in the article. Each section contains a non-text marker.**

1 Name the marker in the second column.
2 Say what it indicates in each case in the third column.

**Example:**

| Section | Non-text marker | Indicates |
|---|---|---|
| 'If you want something doing, do it yourself.' | *speech marks* | *something that people say* |
| 'getting things done ...' | | |
| by *other* people | | |
| (see *Decisions, Decisions, Decisions*) | | |
| MBO | | |
| – miss by a mile | | |

**(10 marks)**

**K** **Find one more example of each non-text marker. What does it indicate in each case?**

**Example:**

| Non-text marker | Example | Indicates |
|---|---|---|
| speech marks | *'Give a person a map, not a route.'* | *something that people say* |
| speech marks | | |
| italics | | |
| brackets | | |
| acronym | | |
| dash | | |

**(10 marks)**

| **Marks out of 100.** | **%** |
|---|---|

# THEME 4 Science and Nature Test

**A Match the words and meanings. Be careful! There is one extra meaning that you don't need.**

**Example:**

| | | |
|---|---|---|
| 1 graph | ______ | not hot or cold |
| 2 laboratory | ______ | the world system of living things |
| 3 scientific | ______ | where information comes from |
| 4 table | ______ | a diagram or drawing in a document |
| 5 test | __1__ | number information in the form of a diagram |
| 6 figure | ______ | a place where experiments are done |
| 7 nature | ______ | the pattern of temperature and rainfall in an area |
| 8 source | ______ | information in columns and rows |
| 9 temperate | ______ | based on science |
| 10 energy | ______ | check; look for something in an experiment |
| 11 ecosystem | ______ | the power to do work |
| | ______ | an area with a particular climate |

**(10 marks)**

**B Find and copy 11 words in the wordsearch. You can read ➔ ➘ ➚.**

**Example:**

| | | | | | | | | | | | |
|---|---|---|---|---|---|---|---|---|---|---|---|
| C | Q | M | Q | E | C | O | L | O | G | Y | L |
| M | A | N | Z | T | F | K | L | L | N | N | W |
| Y | L | R | P | O | L | A | R | D | G | T | R |
| R | Q | G | N | L | C | E | J | C | K | M | Q |
| W | E | B | F | I | T | H | M | Y | T | V | N |
| V | R | Q | P | A | V | Q | C | N | T | M | D |
| Q | Q | O | M | F | X | O | A | H | T | Q | L |
| R | R | I | J | N | Q | L | R | J | A | G | P |
| T | L | L | L | N | P | H | Y | E | N | I | M |
| C | Z | D | W | D | E | S | E | R | T | K | N |
| L | H | B | M | P | Y | R | A | M | I | D | R |
| G | R | Z | H | E | R | B | I | V | O | R | E |

climate ______________ __1__

______________ ___

______________ ___

______________ ___

______________ ___

______________ ___

______________ ___

______________ ___

______________ ___

______________ ___

______________ ___

**(10 marks)**

**C The teacher is going to show you the words from Question B. Write the number of each word in the space above.**

**Example:**

You see: *climate*

You write: *1* beside *climate* **(10 marks)**

**D Copy a word from Question B into each space.**

**Example:**

1 North America has every type of *climate*, from desert to polar.

2 A lion is a ____________________. It eats other animals.

3 Man is at the top of every food ____________________. He does not have any natural predators.

4 Everyone is involved in ____________________. If we do not take an interest, we could destroy the world.

5 The ____________________ areas of the Earth are near the Equator.

6 Secondary consumers are always at the top of a food ____________________. For every one secondary consumer, there are many primary consumers and many, many producers.

7 Most living things are part of a complex food ____________________. A change in any one part can produce many changes in other parts.

**(6 marks)**

**E You have done some research into ecology. Answer these questions.**

1 What is at the bottom of every food chain?

______________________________________________

______________________________________________

2 What actually happens, in scientific terms, in a food chain?

______________________________________________

______________________________________________

3 Why are there always more primary consumers than secondary consumers?

______________________________________________

______________________________________________

4 What animals and plants are in the same food web as a lion?

______________________________________________

______________________________________________

5 What happens if one animal in a food web dies out?

______________________________________________

______________________________________________

**(20 marks)**

**F** **Number these men in chronological order, according to their birth. Use the entries in the *Encyclopedia of Science*.**

| | |
|---|---|
| Charles Darwin | |
| Richard Dawkins | |
| James Lovelock | |
| Gregor Mendel | |

**(4 marks)**

**G** **Find answers to these questions in the *Encyclopedia of Science*.**

1 What is a naturalist?

_______________

_______________

2 What is the difference between an environmentalist and an ecologist?

_______________

_______________

3 Which extra entry should you read to find out more about Darwin's voyage?

_______________

_______________

4 What is a desert, according the **environment** entry?

_______________

_______________

5 What is the best climate habitat for human beings?

_______________

_______________

6 What niche do human beings occupy?

_______________

_______________

**(18 marks)**

**H Is the following information true (✓) or false (✗)? Explain your answers.**

| | | |
|---|---|---|
| 1 Darwin would not have accepted Dawkins' selfish gene theory. | | |
| 2 The Gaia hypothesis is accepted by Dawkins. | | |
| 3 Darwin accepted Gregor Mendel's ideas. | | |

**(12 marks)**

**I Explain, in your own words, the relationship between the following.**

| evolution | genes | heredity | natural selection |
|---|---|---|---|

______________________________________________

______________________________________________

______________________________________________

______________________________________________

______________________________________________

**(10 marks)**

| **Marks out of 100.** | % |
|---|---|

**A Find and copy ten words in the word snake connected with the physical world.**

landscapelatitudelocationlongituderegionborderclimateindustryneighbourcoastline

**Example:**

| | | | |
|---|---|---|---|
| *landscape* | *1* | ____________ | ___ |
| ____________ | ___ | ____________ | ___ |
| ____________ | ___ | ____________ | ___ |
| ____________ | ___ | ____________ | ___ |
| ____________ | ___ | ____________ | ___ |

**(9 marks)**

**B The teacher is going to show you the words from Question A. Write the number of each word in the space above.**

**Example:**

You see: *landscape*
You write: *1* beside *landscape*

**(9 marks)**

**C Match the words and meanings. Be careful! There is one extra meaning that you don't need.**

**Example:**

| | | | |
|---|---|---|---|
| 1 | area | ______ | lake, mountain, river, etc. |
| 2 | natural feature | ______ | damaged building, usually old |
| 3 | agricultural | ______ | where you are going |
| 4 | export | ______ | the normal weather in a particular area |
| 5 | ruin | ______ | people can live there |
| 6 | habitable | *1* | square measurement – length x width |
| 7 | destination | ______ | connected with growing crops or raising animals |
| | | ______ | something sold to another country |

**(6 marks)**

**D You have read about four countries. Tick (✓) true sentences about each country in the correct columns.**

**Example:**

| | Tunisia | Switzerland | Cyprus | Sri Lanka |
|---|---|---|---|---|
| 1 It is in Europe. | | ✓ | ✓ | |
| 2 It is in Asia. | | | | |
| 3 It is in Africa. | | | | |
| 4 It has borders with Algeria and Libya. | | | | |
| 5 It is an island. | | | | |
| 6 It has no coastline. | | | | |
| 7 It is near India. | | | | |
| 8 The Alps range of mountains are in this country. | | | | |
| 9 It has a population of less than a million. | | | | |
| 10 The average temperature is –2°C in January. | | | | |
| 11 There are no permanent lakes or rivers here. | | | | |
| 12 Its most famous export is chocolate. | | | | |

**(12 marks)**

**E Read the text. Complete the table.**

**Example:**

| Country | Wales | Scotland |
|---|---|---|
| | | |
| Continent | *Europe* | *Europe* |
| Borders | | |
| Area | | |
| Population | | |
| Capital | | |
| Languages | | |
| History | | |
| Climate | | |
| Agricultural land | | |
| Highest point | | |
| Lakes and rivers | | |
| Industry and exports | | |

**(42 marks)**

**F** Find each word in the first column in the text.

1 Which part of speech is it – *n*, *v*, *adj* or *adv*?
2 Guess the meaning of the word in context.

**Example:**

| Word or expression | Part of speech | Meaning |
|---|---|---|
| similarities | *n* | *things almost the same* |
| express | | |
| accent | | |
| do it justice | | |
| tops | | |
| rolling | | |
| picturesque | | |
| windswept | | |
| anglers | | |
| char | | |
| left its mark | | |
| remains | | |
| conquer | | |
| officially | | |

**(12 marks)**

**G** What can tourists do in each country? Find three things in each case.

| | Wales | Scotland |
|---|---|---|
| Activity 1 | | |
| Activity 2 | | |
| Activity 3 | | |

**(10 marks)**

| **Marks out of 100.** | % |
|---|---|

**A Read these words. Write each one in the correct column of the table.**

adaptation area beaches behaviour border brain business children coastline decision ecosystem employee evaluate family ~~feature~~ forget habitat husband intelligence landscape manager memory niche parent peak polar process relationship remember revise tropical

**Example:**

| Education | | Daily life | | Work | | Ecology | | The physical world | |
|---|---|---|---|---|---|---|---|---|---|
| | | | | | | | | *feature* | *1* |
| | | | | | | | | | |
| | | | | | | | | | |
| | | | | | | | | | |
| | | | | | | | | | |
| | | | | | | | | | |
| | | | | | | | | | |

**(15 marks)**

**B The teacher is going to show you 11 words from Question A.**
**Write the number of each word in the space above.**

**Example:**
You see: *feature*
You write: *1* beside *feature*

**(10 marks)**

**C Copy a word from Question A into each space. Make any necessary changes.**

**Example:**

You write:

1 The *brain* is not a computer. It does not remember everything we put into it.

2 If you revise things regularly, you will not ________________ them.

3 Regular revision can raise ________________ to 100%.

4 Berne developed a model of the ________________ between people.

5 Thomas Harris said that there are four possible ________________ between two people.

6 It is important to follow a clear ________________ in decision-making.

7 You should generate possible solutions and then ________________ them.

8 An area with a particular climate is called an ________________.

9 The ________________ climate area is north and south of the Equator.

10 All animals show ________________ to their habitat – for example, deep sea fish have very big eyes.

11 What are the most important natural ________________ in your country?

12 The highest ________________ in Switzerland is Pointe Dufour at 4,634 metres.

13 Switzerland is land-locked. It has no ________________ at all.

**(12 marks)**

**D Match words from each column to make phrases.**

**Example:**

| | | | |
|---|---|---|---|
| 1 | vertical | ____ | kilometres |
| 2 | long-term | ____ | links |
| 3 | stimulus- | ____ | style |
| 4 | alternative | *1* | axis |
| 5 | successful | ____ | consumer |
| 6 | management | ____ | temperature |
| 7 | food | ____ | response |
| 8 | primary | ____ | solution |
| 9 | maximum | ____ | memory |
| 10 | transport | ____ | pyramid |
| 11 | square | ____ | possibilities |

**(5 marks)**

**E Match each verb with a possible noun or noun phrase.**

**Example:**

| | | | |
|---|---|---|---|
| 1 | review | ______ | cattle |
| 2 | raise | ______ | a break |
| 3 | take | ______ | an ecosystem |
| 4 | involve | ______ | crops |
| 5 | grow | __*1*__ | information |
| 6 | change | ______ | your mind |
| 7 | destroy | ______ | other people |

**(3 marks)**

**F You have read a lot of information about different subjects in the first five themes. Can you answer these questions?**

**Example:**

1 What percentage of information do you forget within six months if you do no revision at all?

*95%* ______________________________

2 What is the best pattern of revision, to enable you to remember everything?

______________________________

3 What is the most important thing to remember about revision periods?

______________________________

4 What nationality was Eric Berne?

______________________________

5 What nationality was Thomas Harris?

______________________________

6 Name one connection between the two men.

______________________________

7 What is a PC transaction, according to Berne?

______________________________

8 What is the healthiest kind of relationship between two people, according to Harris's model?

______________________________

9 What does the D stand for in the DIGEST method of decision-making?

______________________________

10 What does an autocratic manager do when there is an important decision to be made?

____________________________________________

11 Name three living things in the food web of a lion.

____________________________________________

12 What is at the bottom of every food chain?

____________________________________________

13 In which continent is Tunisia?

____________________________________________

14 Name three countries that border Switzerland.

____________________________________________

15 Name one thing that Tunisia and Switzerland have in common.

____________________________________________

16 Where is Cyprus located?

____________________________________________

17 Where is Sri Lanka located?

____________________________________________

18 Name one thing that Cyprus and Sri Lanka have in common.

____________________________________________

19 What is the most interesting or surprising thing you learnt in this course?

____________________________________________

**(18 marks)**

## G You are going to read a text. Study the title and the diagram. What will the text be about?

______________________________

______________________________

______________________________

______________________________

______________________________

**(2 marks)**

# Are You Securely Attached or Insecure?

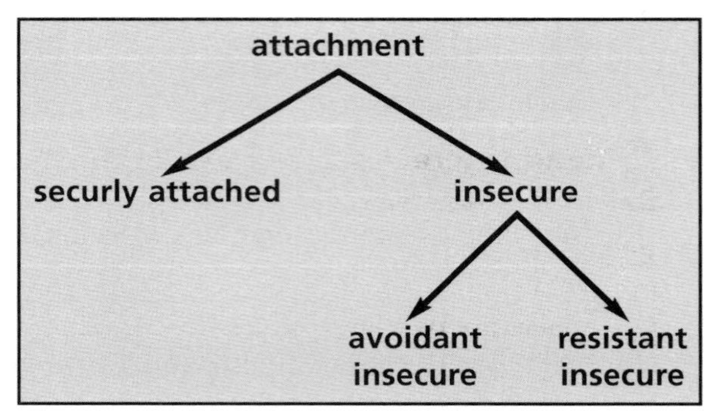


**Figure 1:** ***Categories of attachment***

## H Read the topic sentences 1–5. What do you expect to find in each paragraph?

**Example:**

| Para | Contents |
|---|---|
| 1 | *more about Mary Ainsworth's life* |
| 2 | |
| 3 | |
| 4 | |
| 5 | |

**(4 marks)**

1 Mary Ainsworth was born in 1913 in **Ohio, USA** but her family moved to Canada when she was a child.

2 Ainsworth believed that **infants** can be classified into two main categories.

3 Securely attached infants explore strange environments when their **caregiver** is there.

4 Ainsworth found that the majority of infants in her studies (66%) were securely attached.

5 Other psychologists have adopted Ainsworth's categories and looked at success in later life.

## I Some words in the heading, the figure and the topic sentences may be new to you or may have new meanings in this text. Decide if each word is a noun, a verb or an adjective.

**Example:**

| | n | v | adj |
|---|---|---|---|
| attached | | | ✓ |
| insecure | | | |
| attachment | | | |
| infants | | | |
| explore | | | |
| caregiver | | | |
| studies | | | |
| adopted | | | |

**(7 marks)**

**J** **Read paragraph 1 of the text from a website. You can click on bold words and phrases and get more information. Which bold words will you not click on? List six things.**

**Example:**

1 *Ohio, USA* ______________________ 4 ______________________

2 ______________________ 5 ______________________

3 ______________________ 6 ______________________

**(5 marks)**

**K** **Read the rest of the text. Is the following information true (✓) or false (✗)? Explain your answers.**

**Example:**

| | | |
|---|---|---|
| 1 There are two kinds of insecure attachment. | ✓ | *avoidant and resistant* |
| 2 Infants are very young children. | | |
| 3 Only securely attached infants become upset when the caregiver goes away. | | |
| 4 A caregiver can be male or female. | | |
| 5 In Ainsworth's study, the resistant insecure infants formed the smallest group of infants. | | |
| 6 A study into adolescents took place in 1979. | | |
| 7 Adolescents are older than infants. | | |
| 8 The main difference between the two types of insecure infants is their reaction to the stranger. | | |
| 9 The results of the Hodges and Tizard study are not surprising. | | |

**(8 marks)**

**L** **Read *The Strange Situation*. Answer the questions. You do not need to write full sentences.**

1 What is strange about the situation, for the infant? There are at least three things.

a ______________________________

b ______________________________

c ______________________________

2 At which stages does the securely attached infant feel upset? Work it out.

______________________________

3 Which stage is the most frightening for the child? Choose a stage and explain why.

______________________________

**(6 marks)**

**M** **Which bold words will you click on now to understand more about this topic? Write five words or phrases.**

**Example:**

1 *developmental psychology*

2 ______________________________

3 ______________________________

4 ______________________________

5 ______________________________

6 ______________________________

**(5 marks)**

| Marks out of 100. | % |
|---|---|

**A Match the words and meanings. They are all about money. Be careful! There is one extra meaning that you don't need.**

**Example:**

| | | |
|---|---|---|
| 1 affordable | ____ | use money to buy things |
| 2 amount | ____ | money that you need for something |
| 3 debt | ____ | a sum of money you borrow from a bank |
| 4 loan | *1* | when you have enough money to buy something |
| 5 expenses | ____ | a sum of money you have to pay |
| 6 waste of money | ____ | keep money so that you can use it later |
| 7 save money | ____ | when something costs a lot |
| 8 expensive | ____ | when money is spent in a bad way |
| 9 spend | ____ | how much something is |
| 10 cost | ____ | going without things so you use less money |
| 11 economies | ____ | paying money to borrow something |
| | ____ | a quantity of money or time |

**(10 marks)**

**B Find and copy 11 words and phrases in the wordsearch. You can read → ↘ ↗.**

**Example:**

| | | | | | | | | | | |
|---|---|---|---|---|---|---|---|---|---|---|
| B | B | W | X | M | L | L | D | W | K | C |
| J | Q | T | E | V | A | N | P | E | K | E |
| H | L | G | E | D | A | R | D | T | V | R |
| R | L | F | R | B | D | I | R | I | X | M |
| N | I | Q | S | O | R | I | T | I | R | M |
| W | Z | U | N | B | O | A | N | H | E | D |
| G | H | M | F | M | L | M | P | G | F | D |
| D | C | E | L | E | B | R | A | T | E | H |
| Q | C | E | R | E | M | O | N | Y | P | W |
| K | R | E | C | E | P | T | I | O | N | C |
| M | A | R | R | I | A | G | E | R | W | N |

*bride* ____ *1*

____ ____

____ ____

____ ____

____ ____

____ ____

____ ____

____ ____

____ ____

____ ____

____ ____

**(10 marks)**

**C The teacher is going to show you the words from Question B. Write the number of each word in the space above.**

**Example:**

You see: *bride*

You write: *1* beside *bride*

**(10 marks)**

**D Copy a word from Question B into each space. Make any necessary changes.**

**Example:**

1 In the West, a _*bride*_ usually wears a white dress.

2 Sometimes, in India, the ____________________ family asks for a lot of money.

3 In Britain, you can get ____________________ in a church or in a register office.

4 In a church, the wedding ____________________ takes longer.

5 Sometimes ____________________ can be extremely expensive.

6 Are all your ____________________ coming – even your great grandmother?

7 How many people have you invited to the ____________________?

**(6 marks)**

**E You have read about weddings in different countries in this theme. Answer these questions.**

1 Why are some traditional weddings very expensive?

______________________________________________________________________

______________________________________________________________________

2 Why are some governments stopping marriages between nationals and foreigners?

______________________________________________________________________

______________________________________________________________________

3 Why is bride price illegal in India?

______________________________________________________________________

______________________________________________________________________

4 Why are mass weddings popular in the UAE?

______________________________________________________________________

______________________________________________________________________

5 Why did Nisha's actions appear on the front page of national newspapers in India?

______________________________________________________________________

______________________________________________________________________

**(20 marks)**

**F You are going to read a text.**

1 Read the heading. What will the text be about?

2 Read the introductory paragraph. Check/correct your predictions.

**(2 marks)**

**G Read the topic sentences 1–4. What will be in each paragraph?**

**Example:**

| Para | Contents |
|---|---|
| 1 | *the two kinds of marriage* |
| 2 | |
| 3 | |
| 4 | |

**(6 marks)**

## Marriage all over the world … or all over in 55 hours!

***Where and when can you get married in your country? How many ceremonies do you have to go through? And are the rules the same in other cultures?***

1 Many countries recognize two kinds of marriage.

2 In some countries, couples can opt for a civil ceremony and a religious one.

3 Most countries require marriage ceremonies to be public affairs.

4 Most cultures require notice of a wedding.

**H Read the rest of the text. Is the following information true (✓) or false (✗)? Explain your answers.**

**Example:**

| | | |
|---|---|---|
| 1 In some cultures, you can have a religious ceremony in a hotel room. | ✓ | *it can be consecrated = made into a religious place* |
| 2 In the USA, couples must have a civil ceremony and a religious one. | | |
| 3 In Brazil you must have the civil ceremony before the religious one. | | |
| 4 A marriage ceremony conducted in private is not legal in most countries. | | |
| 5 Spears had only just met the man she married in Las Vegas. | | |

**(8 marks)**

**I Think about each item/idea below.**

1 What is the writer's point of view on each item/idea?
2 Which words in the text helped you work out the point of view?

**Example:**

| Item/idea | What is the writer's point of view? | Which words in the text helped you? |
|---|---|---|
| 1 Civil marriages | *against them* | *just, real, truly* |
| 2 Civil and religious ceremonies at the same time | | |
| 3 The rules about wedding ceremonies in Bulgaria and Holland | | |
| 4 Kylie's wedding plans | | |
| 5 Announcing marriage negotiations over a public address system | | |
| 6 Michael Jackson | | |
| 7 The rules about weddings in Las Vegas | | |

**(24 marks)**

**J** **How do you expect the writer to conclude this article? Choose one of the following conclusions.**

1 Marriage is recognized in most cultures in the world, but there are many important differences in how, where and when you can marry. ___

2 Marriage should be for life, but you need to follow the rules of your culture to make sure you are married in the first place. ___

3 Marriage is not as popular as it used to be in some cultures, but it is still the most common family structure around the world. ___

**(4 marks)**

| **Marks out of 100.** | **%** |
|---|---|

**A Find and copy ten words in the word snake from this theme.**

planetpatentdeviceinventionmaterialinspirationlaboratorydisabilitysatellitetelegraph

**Example:**

*planet* ______ *1*  ______ __
______ __  ______ __
______ __  ______ __
______ __  ______ __
______ __  ______ __

**(9 marks)**

**B The teacher is going to show you the words from Question A. Write the number of each word in the space above.**

**Example:**

You see: *planet*
You write: *1* beside *planet*

**(9 marks)**

**C Match the words and meanings.**

**Example:**

| | | | |
|---|---|---|---|
| 1 | disability | ______ | have an effect on the way someone behaves |
| 2 | genius | ______ | learn words or facts |
| 3 | perspiration | ______ | new and different from anything before |
| 4 | encourage | ______ | very intelligent or artistic |
| 5 | original | *1* | a physical problem so that you can't use part of your body |
| 6 | memorize | ______ | say or do something to help someone succeed |
| 7 | influence | ______ | liquid that appears on your skin when you are hot |

**(6 marks)**

**D You have read about two inventors. How much can you remember about each one?**

**Example:**

| | Thomas Edison | Hedy Lamarr |
|---|---|---|
| 1 Where and when were they born? | *USA, 1847* | |
| 2 When did they die? | | |
| 3 What happened in their youth? | | |
| 4 What jobs did they do? | | |
| 5 What did they invent? | | |
| 6 How successful were their inventions and what did they lead to? | | |
| 7 Add one more fact about each person. | | |

**(26 marks)**

**E You are going to read a text.**

Read the heading. What do you expect to find in the text?

______________________________________

______________________________________

______________________________________

______________________________________

______________________________________

______________________________________

______________________________________

______________________________________

______________________________________

______________________________________

**(4 marks)**

A life of hard work makes office life easier

**F Read the topic sentences 1–10. What do you expect to find in each paragraph?**

**Example:**

| | |
|---|---|
| 1 Chester Floyd Carlson was born in Washington State in the north-west of the USA, on February 8, 1906. | *more about his birth, very early life* |
| 2 The family moved south to find a warmer climate for Chester's parents. | |
| 3 After graduating, he sent 82 different letters before he got a job with the Bell Telephone Company. | |
| 4 In his patent work, he saw the constant need to make copies of patent drawings. | |
| 5 He conducted many experiments at home. | |
| 6 Carlson's invention was based on electrostatics. | |
| 7 In the next six years, Carlson offered his invention to every major office equipment company in the USA. | |
| 8 Battelle didn't like Carlson's name for the invention. | |
| 9 In six months, the company sold more copiers than they expected to sell in 16 years. | |
| 10 Chester Carlson died on September 19, 1968. | |

**(18 marks)**

**G** These statements are true or probably true. Find evidence in the text.

**Example:**

| | |
|---|---|
| 1 Carlson's parents did not have a lot of money. | *He had to work to support them, even as a teenager.* |
| 2 Arthritis and tuberculosis sometimes get better in warmer places. | |
| 3 The Great Depression was a bad time to try to get a job. | |
| 4 Carlson cared about other people, not just himself. | |
| 5 Edison was famous in America in the 1930s. | |
| 6 The Nazis were in power in Germany by 1938. | |
| 7 It was not easy to solve the problems of 'dry copying'. | |
| 8 Photocopiers should be called 'electrocopiers'. | |
| 9 Carlson's invention was an immediate success when it went on sale. | |

**(16 marks)**

**H** Read these 'lessons for life'. Find an example in the text for each one.

| | |
|---|---|
| 1 If at first you don't succeed, try again. | |
| 2 Two heads are better than one. | |
| 3 Concentrate on what you can do, not on what you can't do. | |
| 4 It's nice to be important, but it's more important to be nice. | |
| 5 Only invent things that people want to buy. | |
| 6 Good things come to people who wait for them. | |

**(12 marks)**

| **Marks out of 100.** | **%** |
|---|---|

**A Match the words and meanings. Be careful! There is one extra meaning that you don't need.**

**Example:**

| | | |
|---|---|---|
| 1 anonymous | ______ | when something causes a person's death |
| 2 behaviour | ______ | not usually telling lies |
| 3 entitled | __*1*__ | when we don't know who wrote something |
| 4 faithful | ______ | perfect |
| 5 fatal | ______ | when we give something a name |
| 6 ideal | ______ | very sad |
| 7 moral | ______ | to tell people things they want to hear |
| 8 power | ______ | when you always give support to a person |
| 9 satisfied | ______ | the ability to control people or events |
| 10 tragic | ______ | the way that you do things |
| 11 truthful | ______ | a story that teaches us a lesson about life |
| | ______ | happy or content |

**(10 marks)**

**B Find and copy 11 words in the wordsearch. You can read ➔ ➘ ➚.**

**Example:**

| | | | | | | | | | |
|---|---|---|---|---|---|---|---|---|---|
| M | F | O | R | G | I | V | E | L | D |
| R | E | P | O | R | L | D | F | M | R |
| R | B | V | E | R | A | P | L | O | T |
| T | E | T | E | U | I | R | P | E | T |
| P | L | S | S | N | E | G | C | R | T |
| A | W | R | P | T | T | R | I | I | T |
| B | E | X | T | E | U | H | L | N | T |
| P | C | A | T | O | C | P | X | W | M |
| R | L | H | S | N | S | T | K | Z | M |
| F | M | E | N | V | Y | F | R | F | Q |

*forgive* ______ *1*

______ __
______ __
______ __
______ __
______ __
______ __
______ __
______ __
______ __
______ __

**(10 marks)**

**C The teacher is going to show you the words from Question B. Write the number of each word in the space above.**

**Example:**

You see: *forgive*

You write: *1* beside *forgive*

**(10 marks)**

**D Copy a word from Question B into each space. Make any necessary changes.**

**Example:**

1 The *plot* of *King Lear* may be about a real person.

2 Shakespeare often used several different ________________ for a play.

3 I've no idea what the ________________ of the story are – I mean, where it comes from.

4 Don't let people ________________ you to do something if you don't want to.

5 Shakespeare believed that children should ________________ their parents.

6 He stole all my money so I can't ________________ him.

7 There was a big sports ________________ in the park yesterday.

**(6 marks)**

**E You have read about two Shakespeare plays. Complete each sentence with something true for each play.**

**Example:**

| | Julius Caesar | King Lear |
|---|---|---|
| 1 Shakespeare wrote the play in around … | *1599* | *1605–08* |
| 2 One of his sources for the play was … | | |
| 3 The play is based on the life of the leader of … | | |
| 4 The real person lived around … | | |
| 5 One of the female characters is called … | | |
| 6 She is … | | |
| 7 One of the other male characters is called … | | |
| 8 He is … | | |
| 9 The main character dies because … | | |
| 10 The play is about … | | |

**(18 marks)**

**F You are going to read about a Shakespeare play.**

Write five research questions.

**Example:**

| Research question | Section |
|---|---|
| 1 When did Shakespeare write the play? | *a* |
| 2 | |
| 3 | |
| 4 | |
| 5 | |
| 6 | |

**(5 marks)**

**G Read the heading. What does it mean?**

**A Noble Betrayal**

______________________________________

______________________________________

______________________________________

______________________________________

______________________________________

______________________________________

(Note: You will have a chance to come back and answer this question after reading the text.)

**(3 marks)**

**H Read the section headings.**

Which section will probably contain the answer to each of your research questions? Write the letter of the section after each research question in Question F above. If you do not think there is a suitable section, put *???*.

**(5 marks)**

a 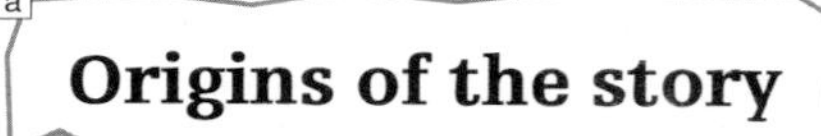


b **The real Coriolanus**

c **The play**

d **The themes**

**I Read the text. Who or what is each of the names below?**

**Example:**

| | |
|---|---|
| 1 Gaius Marcius | *the real name of Coriolanus* |
| 2 Corioli | |
| 3 Volscia | |
| 4 Aufidius | |
| 5 Volumnia | |

**(8 marks)**

## J Who does what?

**Example:**

Who:

| | |
|---|---|
| 1 captures Corioli? | *Gaius Marcius/Coriolanus* |
| 2 persuades Coriolanus to run for Consul? | |
| 3 exiles Coriolanus? | |
| 4 makes an agreement with Aufidius to attack Rome? | |
| 5 persuades Coriolanus to make peace with Rome? | |
| 6 kills Coriolanus? | |

**(10 marks)**

## K The writer refers to the following items in different ways in the text. Find one other way in each case.

**Example:**

| | |
|---|---|
| 1 Gaius Marcius | *a Roman general* |
| 2 Rome | |
| 3 Consul | |
| 4 ordinary people | |
| 5 Aufidius | |
| 6 aristocracy | |

**(5 marks)**

## L Complete the table with the missing words. They all appear in the text.

**Example:**

| Verb | Related noun |
|---|---|
| 1 persuade | *persuasion* |
| 2 approve | |
| 3 elect | |
| 4 endorse | |
| 5 refuse | |
| 6 exile | |
| 7 attack | |
| 8 try | |
| 9 betray | |
| 10 respect | |
| 11 destroy | |

**(10 marks)**

| Marks out of 100. | % |
|---|---|

**A Find and copy ten words in the word snake connected with sports and leisure.**

footballcourtobjectiveequipmentoriginatekickedlocationceremoniestennisracing

**Example:**

*football* ________ *1*

________ ___ ________ ___

________ ___ ________ ___

________ ___ ________ ___

________ ___ ________ ___

________ ___

**(9 marks)**

**B The teacher is going to show you the words from Question A. Write the number of each word in the space above.**

**Example:**

You see: *football*

You write: *1* beside *football*

**(9 marks)**

**C Match the words and meanings.**

**Example:**

| | |
|---|---|
| 1 aim | ___ very old |
| 2 ancient | ___ things you must or must not do |
| 3 document | ___ you need two of these at each end of the court for basketball |
| 4 team | ___ things you need to play a particular game |
| 5 rules | ___ doing things that hurt other people |
| 6 violence | *1* the same meaning as *objective* |
| 7 post | ___ a piece of paper with important information on it |
| | ___ a group of people who play a game or sport together |

**(6 marks)**

**D You have read about the history of football. How much can you remember about it?**

Write short answers for each question. Give as much information as possible.

**Example:**

1 In ancient times, what did the words *tsu chu* and *aqsaqtuk* mean?

*They are ancient words for 'football' type games.*

2 What did ancient peoples use for a ball?

______________________________

______________________________

3 Which countries or areas played a kind of football in the past?

______________________________

______________________________

4 Where did people play forerunners of football?

______________________________

______________________________

5 How many people sometimes played?

______________________________

______________________________

6 Why did several kings of England try to stop the game?

______________________________

______________________________

**(15 marks)**

**E You have read about the history of horse racing. Find the best way to complete each sentence about the sport.**

**Example:**

| | | | |
|---|---|---|---|
| 1 | People started to tame wild horses | ______ | to the Romans. |
| 2 | Then people used horses to help them | ______ | to Spain. |
| 3 | The first record of horse riding comes | *1* | in about 3700 BCE. |
| 4 | People in Egypt were riding horses | ______ | to Britain in 208 AD. |
| 5 | The Greeks were also riding horses | ______ | at the 23rd Olympics. |
| 6 | Horse racing with riders appeared | ______ | by 1580 BCE. |
| 7 | The Greeks taught horse racing | ______ | with farming. |
| 8 | The Romans introduced horse racing | ______ | 200 years later. |
| 9 | The Arabs introduced faster horses | ______ | from Persia. |

**(16 marks)**

**F You are going to read a text.**

Read the heading and the subheading and look at the illustration. Can you work out the topic of the text?

________________________________________

________________________________________

________________________________________

________________________________________

**(6 marks)**

**G Read the topic sentences 1–8. What do you expect to find in each paragraph?**

**Example:**

| Para | Contents |
|---|---|
| 1 | *more about the sport in general – perhaps the name of the sport?* |
| 2 | |
| 3 | |
| 4 | |
| 5 | |
| 6 | |
| 7 | |
| 8 | |

**(7 marks)**

# Creag-a-wicket

**THEY PROBABLY DIDN'T INVENT IT,
THEY DON'T USUALLY WIN IT,
BUT IT IS STILL THE NATIONAL GAME OF ENGLAND.**

1. It's the national sport of England.

2. Many people think cricket originated *outside* England.

3. However, some historians believe that cricket started as a children's game in southern England.

4. Many researchers believe that the game developed from bowls.

5. Perhaps shepherds developed the game on the hillsides of old England as they looked after their sheep.

6. What about the name of the game itself?

7. England started to export the game in 1789.

8. After years of trying, Australia finally beat an English team in England.

**H Read the text. Make a timeline of events in the history of cricket. Only include *facts*, not *theories*. Use notes, not full sentences.**

**Example:**

| Date | Event |
|---|---|
| 8th/9th C | bat + ball games in Med. cntries |
| | |
| | |
| | |
| | |
| | |
| | |
| | |

**(7 marks)**

**I When you do research, one article never gives you all the answers. Make notes of one extra piece of information you want after reading each paragraph.**

**Example:**

| Para | Extra information |
|---|---|
| 1 | why Sun.; village green = ? |
| | |
| | |
| | |
| | |
| | |
| | |
| | |

**(14 marks)**

**J What exactly is the writer referring to with the words in italics?**

**Example:**

| | | |
|---|---|---|
| Para 1 | It's *the national sport.* | *cricket* |
| Para 2 | when *they* invaded in 1066, … | |
| Para 3 | From *there*, … | |
| Para 3 | A man died in *that year* … | |
| Para 4 | In *that game*, … | |
| Para 4 | to stop the ball hitting *it*. | |
| Para 5 | *This explains* the current cricketing terms … | |
| Para 6 | *It* could refer to the bat. | |
| Para 6 | *This word* probably gave its name … | |
| Para 7 | the revolution started *that year* … | |
| Para 7 | and *they* had to come home … | |
| Para 8 | *which* died at the Oval … | |

**(11 marks)**

| **Marks out of 100.** | **%** |
|---|---|

**A Match the words and meanings. Be careful! There is one extra meaning that you don't need.**

**Example:**

|  | |  |
|---|---|---|
| 1 energy | ______ | salt |
| 2 carbohydrate | ______ | the opposite of positive |
| 3 protein | *1* | strength to do work or actions |
| 4 fibre | ______ | keep two things at the same level or amount |
| 5 sodium | ______ | it is in food such as meat, fish and beans |
| 6 balance | ______ | when there is not enough food to live |
| 7 reduce | ______ | it helps food move quickly through your body |
| 8 nutrition | ______ | having the right kind of food for good health |
| 9 calories | ______ | it is in food such as bread, rice and potatoes |
| 10 starvation | ______ | measure, find out the amount |
| 11 negative | ______ | a way of measuring the amount of energy in food |
| | ______ | make something smaller or less |

**(10 marks)**

**B Find and copy 11 words and phrases in the wordsearch. You can read → ↘ ↗.**

**Example:**

| | | | | | | | | | | | |
|---|---|---|---|---|---|---|---|---|---|---|---|
| E | G | H | K | X | Z | M | L | T | S | J | P |
| P | Q | M | E | X | K | A | S | E | X | L | T |
| T | K | U | L | A | C | R | L | U | M | K | T |
| N | D | N | A | I | L | C | X | C | G | H | K |
| L | M | L | S | L | S | T | N | N | Z | A | R |
| W | V | Y | T | U | N | L | H | Y | V | Q | R |
| J | H | T | M | U | A | W | E | I | G | H | T |
| P | N | L | O | R | X | T | M | F | Q | W | G |
| B | Q | M | E | Q | H | J | M | K | W | C | T |
| D | A | N | T | V | I | T | A | M | I | N | K |
| B | I | C | A | L | C | U | L | A | T | E | K |
| M | D | Y | T | I | N | C | R | E | A | S | E |

*equal* ______ *1*

______ __

______ __

______ __

______ __

______ __

______ __

______ __

______ __

______ __

______ __

**(10 marks)**

**C The teacher is going to show you the words from Question B. Write the number of each word in the space on the left.**

**Example:**

You see: *equal*
You write: *1* beside *equal*

**(10 marks)**

**D Copy a word or phrase from Question B into each space. Make any necessary changes.**

**Example:**

1 Your daily energy in should *equal* your daily energy out.
2 You need to lose fat, not ____________________, if you go on a diet.
3 Your body needs ____________________ such as calcium and magnesium for good health.
4 I really need to do more ____________________ activity to lose weight.
5 The ____________________ of food you need gets less as you get older.
6 It's easy to ____________________ your daily calorie requirement.
7 I'd like to ____________________ the time I spend at the gym, but it's difficult.

**(6 marks)**

**E Read these words. Write each one in the correct column of the table.**

border brain climate evaluate experiment laboratory memory ~~parent~~
plot population reception relationship select theme tropical wedding

**Example:**

| Learning | Families | Making decisions | Weather |
|---|---|---|---|
| | *parent* | | |
| | | | |
| | | | |
| **Countries** | **Marriage** | **Inventions** | **Theatre** |
| | | | |
| | | | |

**(15 marks)**

**F How much information can you remember from the course? Answer each question.**

1 What is the best way to revise?

______________________________

2 Who were Eric Berne and Thomas Harris?

______________________________

3 What is the DIGEST approach to decision-making?

______________________________

______________________________

4 What is a food chain?

______________________________

5 Why is Switzerland a good place for a holiday?

______________________________

6 Why are weddings expensive?

______________________________

7 Who was Hedy Lamarr?

______________________________

8 Which Shakespeare play is about a Roman general?

______________________________

9 How old is the game of football?

______________________________

10 What is the best way to lose weight?

______________________________

______________________________

**(20 marks)**

**G You are going to read a text. Read the heading and look at the illustration.**

Can you work out the topic of the text?

______________________________

______________________________

______________________________

______________________________

**(2 marks)**

**H Read the introduction. What subtopics do you expect to read about?**

______________________________

______________________________

______________________________

______________________________

______________________________

______________________________

**(3 marks)**

**I Read the topic sentences 1–7. What do you expect to find in each paragraph?**

| Para | Contents |
|---|---|
| 1 | *definitions of the two types of exercise* |
| 2 | |
| 3 | |
| 4 | |
| 5 | |
| 6 | |
| 7 | |

**(6 marks)**

# *How do you take your exercise? With oxygen, or without?*

*You know that you should take exercise on a regular basis. But what kind of exercise should you do? To some extent, it depends on your objective. Do you want to lose weight, get fit or just get stronger? It's all a matter of oxygen.*

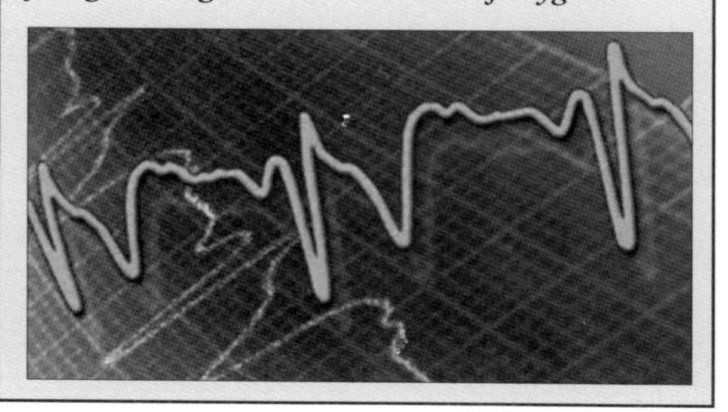

1 There are two basic types of exercise.

2 When you exercise for a period of time, your body moves between the two types.

3 What actually happens in your body when you start to exercise?

4 If you continue to exercise, the process changes.

5 After about 20 minutes, there is another change.

6 However, if you push your body very hard at any point, it will switch to anaerobic processing.

7 If you want to get all the benefits of exercise, you should force the body to use aerobic and anaerobic processes.

**J** Read the first two paragraphs. Think also about your own experience. Answer the questions. Some information is in the text, but you will have to infer some information.

1 How do you know that your body is working anaerobically?

______________________________________________

2 When does the body switch to anaerobic exercise?

______________________________________________

3 How long can you, personally, exercise anaerobically?

______________________________________________

**(3 marks)**

**K** Read the rest of the text. Complete Table 1.

Table 1: *Energy source and value of different stages of exercise*

| | Time from start of exercise (mins) | | | |
|---|---|---|---|---|
| | 1–3 | 4–20 | 20+ | any time |
| Type of exercise | *anaerobic* | | | *anaerobic* |
| Example | | *walking* | *walking* | *sprinting* |
| Energy source | *sugar in the muscles* | | *sugar in fat* | |
| Value of exercise | | *makes heart and lungs work better* | | |

**(8 marks)**